One Solitary Life

Christ in the Synoptic Gospels

One Solitary Life

Christ in the Synoptic Gospels

REGULAR BAPTIST PRESS
1300 North Meacham Road
Schaumburg, Illinois 60173-4806

This inductive Bible study is designed for individual, small group, or classroom use. A leader's guide with full lesson plans and the answers to the Bible study questions is available from Regular Baptist Press. Order RBP1629 online at www.regularbaptistpress.org, e-mail orders@rbpstore.org, call toll free at 1-800-727-4440, or contact your distributor.

ONE SOLITARY LIFE: CHRIST IN THE SYNOPTIC GOSPELS
Adult Bible Study Book
Vol. 53, No. 1
© 2004
Regular Baptist Press • Schaumburg, Illinois
1-800-727-4440 • www.regularbaptistpress.org
Printed in U.S.A.
All rights reserved
RBP1629 • 1-59402-146-5

Contents

Preface

This study is designed to help us discover how the Lord Jesus Christ was truly, fully Man and yet set apart, solitary, unique in His life and work. There was never another man like Jesus, and there never will be. What He accomplished was essential to mankind's deliverance from sin. No one else could do what Jesus did.

Was there ever a life so filled with knowledge, understanding, love, compassion, energy, power, and personality? His very perfections set Him apart and often compelled Him to live a life marked by aloneness—not loneliness in the sense of being forlorn, but alone in that His companions were unable to understand or appreciate what set Him apart from other men. His parents did not understand Him; He went alone to the temple so He could converse with Jewish leaders about His Father's business. His brothers and sisters did not understand Him; they did not listen to Him or believe Him. The more He manifested His uniqueness, the more people were troubled by Him. In our human nature, we are often reassured by what is familiar and fearful of what is different. Jesus Christ walked a lonely path even in the midst of the crowds that often surrounded Him.

This study will challenge you to go beyond a casual experience of believing in Christ out of a sense of duty. It will nurture the desire and growing conviction that Christ's "life was manifested, and we have seen it" (1 John 1:2). It is with this personal conviction that we share this living Christ with those who do not know Him.

Introduction

People who have read and compared the four gospel accounts have discovered that three of them—Matthew, Mark, and Luke—contain a lot of similar material, while much that John recorded in the Gospel of John is not found in any of the other Gospels.

Synoptic Gospels

People often study the first three Gospels together because they are the "synoptic Gospels," a term derived from Greek words that mean "to see together." Scholars refer to a synoptic "problem" caused by questions about the similarities and differences within these Gospels—questions such as, Why do the first three Gospels have so much in common? (For example, 610 of the 661 verses in Mark are contained in Matthew and Luke.) Did the writers copy from one another, or were the Gospels independently written? What caused them to have material common to all three, common to only two, and material contained in only one of the Gospels? What was the Holy Spirit's purpose in arranging the content of the Gospels in this way?

Gospel Writers

People have speculated about how these Gospels were written. Personal contact was one source for the content of the gospel accounts. The apostle Matthew closely associated with Christ throughout His earthly ministry. Mark lived in Jerusalem, engaged in missionary work with Paul and Barnabas, and closely associated with Peter, from whom he would have received firsthand accounts of the life of Christ.

The apostles were established in Jerusalem during the time represented by the first seven chapters of Acts. The information they possessed about the life of Christ would have been shared and repeated. Matthew, Mark, and Luke would also naturally have taken care to examine written records, as Luke specifically stated that he did (Luke 1:1–4; Acts 1:1–3).

Still more significant than the efforts of these men is the promise of Christ: "But the Comforter, which is the Holy Ghost, whom the Father will send in my name, he shall teach you all things, and bring all things to your remembrance, whatsoever I have said unto you" (John 14:26). The Holy Spirit enabled the gospel writers to discover the written records, to evaluate them, to remember from personal contact with Christ or from those who had heard Him, and then to relate those things to us accurately, without error.

Repetition in the Synoptic Gospels

If the gospel accounts contained no repetition, critics would say that an editor had corrected the manuscripts to make sure that each one contained new material. However, where there is repetition, critics say that two of the writers must have copied from the third. This speculation reduces the inspired Scripture to a human level and attributes to an unknown editor what the Bible attributes to the Holy Spirit.

The repetition, instead, emphasizes certain themes and provides more than one witness to the event. Scripture tells us that the testimony of two or three witnesses will establish a matter (Deuteronomy 19:15; cf. Matthew 18:16). God has given us three witnesses plus one extra! Each writer did not need to consult the others but independently wrote what he, being led by the Holy Spirit (2 Peter 1:21), believed was important. The writers possibly would have deleted their repetitive passages if they had consulted one another. Some of the passages contain slight differences (not contradictions), which indicate the separate witnesses to the event and provide additional information. You will want to study the "Comparative Chart of the Gospels" on page 11 to discover the writers' themes, their approaches, and more. You might also find it helpful to use a harmony of the Gospels throughout this study. Some study Bibles contain a harmony in outline form, or you can purchase a harmony in book form.

Looking at the Lord Jesus Christ through the threefold synoptic Gospels provides a picture of Him that is truly three-dimensional. We see the height of His human perfection, the breadth of His miraculous ministry, and the depth of His divine love.

COMPARATIVE CHART OF THE GOSPELS

Concept	Matthew	Mark	Luke	John
Time focus	Past, Old Testament	Present	Future	Eternity
The "Branch" of Isaiah 11:1–5 seen as . . .	King (Jeremiah 23:5, 6)	Servant (Zechariah 3:8)	Man (Zechariah 6:12)	Beautiful and glorious in that day (Isaiah 4:2)
Intended audience	Jews	Romans, Gentiles	Greeks, world	Church
Emphasis	Prophetic, didactic	Practical, anecdotal	Historical (Luke 1:1–4)	Spiritual
Christ seen as . . .	Mighty King, Messiah	Lowly Servant	Son of Man, Ideal Man	Son of God
Main theme	Royalty	Power	Love	Proof

Synoptic Gospels Reading Guide

By reading about two chapters a day, you can read through the synoptic Gospels three times in three months. Commit to reading these books as you study *One Solitary Life*.

_____ Day 1: Matthew 1:1—3:12

_____ Day 2: Matthew 3:13—5:20

_____ Day 3: Matthew 5:21—7:29

_____ Day 4: Matthew 8:1—10:4

_____ Day 5: Matthew 10:5—12:21

_____ Day 6: Matthew 12:22—14:36

_____ Day 7: Matthew 15:1—17:13

_____ Day 8: Matthew 17:14—19:30

_____ Day 9: Matthew 20:1—22:14

_____ Day 10: Matthew 22:15—24:35

_____ Day 11: Matthew 24:36—26:56

_____ Day 12: Matthew 26:57—28:20

_____ Day 13: Mark 1:1—3:6

_____ Day 14: Mark 3:7—5:20

_____ Day 15: Mark 5:21—7:23

_____ Day 16: Mark 7:24—9:13

_____ Day 17: Mark 9:14—11:11

_____ Day 18: Mark 11:12—13:37

_____ Day 19: Mark 14:1—16:20

_____ Day 20: Luke 1:1—3:6

_____ Day 21: Luke 3:7—5:11

_____ Day 22: Luke 5:12—7:17

_____ Day 23: Luke 7:18—9:27

_____ Day 24: Luke 9:28—11:28

_____ Day 25: Luke 11:29—13:5

_____ Day 26: Luke 13:6—15:10

_____ Day 27: Luke 15:11—17:10

_____ Day 28: Luke 17:11—19:10

_____ Day 29: Luke 19:11—21:28

_____ Day 30: Luke 21:29—22:65

_____ Day 31: Luke 22:66—24:53

_____ Day 32: Matthew 1:1—3:12

_____ Day 33: Matthew 3:13—5:20

_____ Day 34: Matthew 5:21—7:29

_____ Day 35: Matthew 8:1—10:4

_____ Day 36: Matthew 10:5—12:21

_____ Day 37: Matthew 12:22—14:36

_____ Day 38: Matthew 15:1—17:13

_____ Day 39: Matthew 17:14—19:30

_____ Day 40: Matthew 20:1—22:14

_____ Day 41: Matthew 22:15—24:35

_____ Day 42: Matthew 24:36—26:56

_____ Day 43: Matthew 26:57—28:20

_____ Day 44: Mark 1:1—3:6

_____ Day 45: Mark 3:7—5:20

_____ Day 46: Mark 5:21—7:23

_____ Day 47: Mark 7:24—9:13

_____ Day 48: Mark 9:14—11:11

_____ Day 49: Mark 11:12—13:37

_____ Day 50: Mark 14:1—16:20

_____ Day 51: Luke 1:1—3:6

_____ Day 52: Luke 3:7—5:11

_____ Day 53: Luke 5:12—7:17

_____ Day 54: Luke 7:18—9:27

_____ Day 55: Luke 9:28—11:28

_____ Day 56: Luke 11:29—13:5

_____ Day 57: Luke 13:6—15:10

_____ Day 58: Luke 15:11—17:10

_____ Day 59: Luke 17:11—19:10

_____ Day 60: Luke 19:11—21:28

_____ Day 61: Luke 21:29—22:65

_____ Day 62: Luke 22:66—24:53

_____ Day 63: Matthew 1:1—3:12

_____ Day 64: Matthew 3:13—5:20

_____ Day 65: Matthew 5:21—7:29

_____ Day 66: Matthew 8:1—10:4

_____ Day 67: Matthew 10:5—12:21

_____ Day 68: Matthew 12:22—14:36

_____ Day 69: Matthew 15:1—17:13

_____ Day 70: Matthew 17:14—19:30

_____ Day 71: Matthew 20:1—22:14

_____ Day 72: Matthew 22:15—24:35

_____ Day 73: Matthew 24:36—26:56

_____ Day 74: Matthew 26:57—28:20

_____ Day 75: Mark 1:1—3:6

_____ Day 76: Mark 3:7—5:20

_____ Day 77: Mark 5:21—7:23

_____ Day 78: Mark 7:24—9:13

_____ Day 79: Mark 9:14—11:11

_____ Day 80: Mark 11:12—13:37

_____ Day 81: Mark 14:1—16:20

_____ Day 82: Luke 1:1—3:6

_____ Day 83: Luke 3:7—5:16

_____ Day 84: Luke 5:17—7:35

_____ Day 85: Luke 7:36—9:50

_____ Day 86: Luke 9:51—11:54

_____ Day 87: Luke 12:1—14:14

_____ Day 88: Luke 14:15—16:18

_____ Day 89: Luke 16:19—18:30

_____ Day 90: Luke 18:31—20:47

_____ Day 91: Luke 21:1—22:65

_____ Day 92: Luke 22:63—24:53

Begotten Alone:
Incarnation

"Now all this was done, that it might be fulfilled which was spoken of the Lord by the prophet, saying, Behold, a virgin shall be with child, and shall bring forth a son, and they shall call his name Emmanuel, which being interpreted is, God with us" (Matthew 1:22, 23).

Istory? Who likes *history?*" "I hate history!"
These exact quotes are from students weary of memorizing dates, names of places, and names of people. But we benefit from reading of the successes of the past so we may repeat them and from reading of the failures of the past so we may avoid them.

Paul emphasized this reality in 1 Corinthians 10:11, warning us of Israel's failure: "Now all these things happened unto them *for ensamples:* and they were written *for our admonition,* upon whom the ends of the world are come" (italics added).

Studying the Bible requires understanding the times in which the Scriptures were written. As we approach the study of the life of Christ, we need to know about the world He came to live in.

Getting Started

1. Around the year of your birth, what world events were occurring? Who were key leaders at the time? What common values did people hold?

2. In what ways are our lives shaped by the world into which we are born?

Searching the Scriptures

3. From the time of mankind's fall into sin, God had promised to send a Redeemer. What do Galatians 4:4 and 5 tell us about when and why God chose to send His Son into the world?

At the time of Christ, Israel looked back to a rich heritage of deliverance. God had made Israel the instrument through which He could share many blessings with the world. However, Israel failed in that task. By the time of Christ, the Pharisees had added to the body of truth in such a way that they effectively concealed the truth that their additions were expected to expose! So, to large segments of Israel, the Jewish religion was merely empty hope. It was into this vacuum in a hollow world that Jesus came.

The life of Christ is recorded in four Gospels: Matthew, Mark, Luke, and John. The first three Gospels are often studied together because they share so much similar material. They are called the "synoptic" Gospels because "synoptic" comes from Greek words that mean "to see together." Matthew, Mark, and Luke "see together," as three witnesses, the life and ministry of Jesus Christ. But the Gospel of John is quite different from the first three gospel accounts.

4. What might explain the existence of four Gospels instead of just one comprehensive account of the life, teachings, death, and resurrection of Jesus?

5. What are benefits of having three gospel accounts that present similar, but unique, perspectives of the life and ministry of Jesus?

6. According to the following passages, for what particular qualities, character, or deeds were the Jews looking to fulfill the Old Testament promises of God?

   a. Luke 7:16–20

   b. Luke 24:21

   c. Acts 1:6

   d. 2 Samuel 7:12, 13

   e. Isaiah 9:6, 7

7. What did Jesus' contemporaries recognize about His human identity?

   a. Matthew 15:22; 20:29–31

b. Matthew 21:11

c. Mark 6:3

8. Read and mark your place in Genesis 3:15. Now read Isaiah 7:14. How does the prophecy of Isaiah relate to the promise in Genesis 3?

9. When Jesus was born, who actually knew that He was fulfilling Isaiah 7:14? See Matthew 1:18–25 and Luke 1:26–45.

10. According to Matthew 1:21–23 and John 1:14, what would this Child be able to do because He was God incarnate, God become man?

11. List some appropriate ways to welcome and greet the One qualified to fulfill the prophecies you have considered.

12. How did the following people respond to Christ's arrival?
a. Mary (Luke 1:28–56)

b. Joseph (Matthew 1:18–25)

c. Elisabeth (Luke 1:39–45)

d. Zacharias (Luke 1:59–79)

e. Shepherds (Luke 2:8–20)

f. Simeon (Luke 2:21–35)

g. Anna (Luke 2:36–38)

h. Wise men (Matthew 2:1–12)

i. Herod (Matthew 2:1–16)

j. Chief priests and scribes (Matthew 2:4–23)

Making It Personal

13. How have you responded to Christ's coming into the world?

___ I'm still considering how to respond.

___ I have admitted I am a sinner (Romans 3:23).

___ I have repented from my sin (Romans 6:22, 23).

___ I believe that Jesus Christ died, was buried, and rose from the dead for me (Romans 10:9).

___ I have asked Jesus to be my personal Savior (Romans 10:13).

14. If you have welcomed Christ into your life as your personal Savior, what aspects of your attitudes and actions show that He is your Savior?

15. What attitudes and actions do you need to change in order to demonstrate to others the reality of Christ's work in your life?

He Fought Alone:
Temptation

"For we have not an high priest which cannot be touched with the feeling of our infirmities; but was in all points tempted like as we are, yet without sin" (Hebrews 4:15).

Have you ever wondered what Jesus was like as a child? The Bible tells us little about that time, while it records a great deal about the three years of His public ministry and even reveals some prophecy concerning His future. How did Jesus go from the quiet seclusion of a country village to active public ministry? He made the transition through two experiences: one public, the other private. In His public baptism by John the Baptist and His private temptation by Satan, we discover the signs of His deity and the relationship between His humanity and His deity.

Getting Started

1. List at least ten words or phrases that tend to describe children.

2. Which of the descriptions probably characterized Jesus in His childhood?

Searching the Scriptures

3. Luke 2:40 and 52 tell about Jesus' growth as a boy.

   a. Why do you think it would be important for the Son of God to grow in the characteristics mentioned in these verses?

   b. Why do you think it would be important for Him to grow in favor with both God and the people around Him?

When Jesus was twelve years old, His family traveled to Jerusalem to celebrate the Passover and also His coming of age as the eldest son. Luke 2:41–51 describes that trip.

4. Luke 2:47 indicates that "all [who] heard him were astonished at his understanding and answers." What does their astonishment indicate about the questions Jesus raised and the answers He gave?

5. Mary asked, "Son, why has thou thus dealt with us? behold, thy father and I have sought thee sorrowing" (Luke 2:48). What did Jesus' response reveal about His consciousness of His true identity (v. 49)?

In spite of His understanding of Who He is and what He'd come to earth to do, the young Jesus returned to the routine of life at Nazareth, where He was obedient to Mary and Joseph (Luke 2:51).

In the meantime, God was working in the life and heart of a boy named John, who grew up to be the man we know as John the Baptist.

6. a. How did John the Baptist differ from most men of his day, as revealed in Matthew 3:4, Mark 1:6, and Luke 1:15?

b. How did John the Baptist fulfill his mission (Matthew 3:1–3, 5, 6; Mark 1:4–6; Luke 1:15, 76–80)?

c. Why might some of the people have wondered if John were the Messiah (Luke 3:15; Isaiah 42:1–4; 53:1–3; Jeremiah 23:5, 6; Zechariah 6:12)?

John's preaching was like the necessary plow that breaks up the earth so the seed can be sown and a crop harvested. John prepared the way for, in his own words, "one mightier than I" (Luke 3:16).

One day while John was preaching and baptizing, Jesus Christ came along.

7. a. Why did John feel inadequate to baptize Jesus (Matthew 3:13–15; John 1:29–33)?

b. How did God use Jesus' baptism to give Jesus authority (Mark 1:9–11; John 1:32, 33)?

Jesus insisted on being baptized because He identified with humanity in every other way and because He performed all the duties that a spiritually minded Jew would do.

8. Explain how Jesus' baptism was important to the following people.

a. John the Baptist

b. The crowd at the Jordan

c. Jesus Himself

After Jesus' baptism, the Holy Spirit led Jesus into the wilderness to be tempted by Satan.

9. Read Matthew 4:1–11 and Genesis 3:1–7.

a. How were Satan's tactics in tempting Jesus similar to the methods he used with Adam and Eve?

b. Based on Christ's answer to each of Satan's temptations, describe why each situation would have been a temptation for Christ.

c. Hebrews 4:15 states that Christ "was in all points tempted like as we are." In what ways were His temptations like the temptations we face every day? In what respects were they unique?

10. Based on Christ's handling of each temptation, what conclusions can you draw about using Scripture to overcome temptation?

Making It Personal

11. What do these passages teach you about temptation and how to address it successfully?

    a. 1 Corinthians 10:13

    b. Hebrews 2:18

    c. Hebrews 4:15, 16

Christ used God's Word to overcome temptation. But to use the Word of God as a weapon against temptation, we must hide God's Word in our hearts (Psalm 119:11).

12. What practical step will you take this week to improve your ability to use God's Word against temptations?

Lesson 3

He Cared Alone:
Compassion

"The Spirit of the Lord is upon me, because he hath anointed me to preach the gospel to the poor; he hath sent me to heal the brokenhearted, to preach deliverance to the captives, and recovering of sight to the blind, to set at liberty them that are bruised, to preach the acceptable year of the Lord" (Luke 4:18, 19).

You have no doubt seen advertisements on TV for charitable organizations, and you may have seen similar ads in magazines. They picture children in underdeveloped, war-torn, or disaster-struck nations who need food, clothing, schooling, and health care. The ads are clearly designed to stir our compassion and motivate us to give.

God has great compassion for suffering people. But more than that, He had so much compassion for the entire sinful human race that He gave the ultimate Gift, His Son, to die on the cross to take the penalty for our sin. Jesus came "to seek and to save that which was lost" (Luke 19:10). However, He did not ignore the suffering around Him while He waited to die as our Substitute. He demonstrated compassion through His power and His love.

Getting Started

1. Have you ever used your strength, authority, or influence to help someone on whom you had compassion?

   a. If so, summarize the experience.

   b. If not, has anyone showed you compassion by using his or her strength, authority, or influence on your behalf? Summarize that experience.

2. a. In your opinion, what is a miracle?

   b. How does your dictionary define "miracle"?

3. Do you think people would have recognized Jesus' deity if He had not done miraculous works? Why or why not?

Searching the Scriptures

4. a. Read Matthew 8:23–27, Mark 4:35–41, and Luke 8:22–25. What differences and similarities do you observe in the various accounts?

b. How does having more than perspective deepen your understanding of the recorded event?

5. a. Read Matthew 14:13–21 and Luke 7:11–17. What made each of
these miracles important from a human perspective?

b. In what ways did each miracle reveal Christ's compassion for
people's circumstances?

Jesus demonstrated His compassionate *power* by delivering people
from nature, sickness, demons, and even death. He also demonstrated
His compassionate *love* in this way.

6. How does Luke 4:14–21 explain why Jesus performed miracles?

7. In Luke 7:18–22 John the Baptist sent some of his disciples to
double-check with Jesus that He really was the Messiah, the One Israel
had been waiting for. Why would Jesus' miracles (vv. 20, 21) be a suffi-
cient answer to John the Baptist's questions and doubts?

Making It Personal

8. When Christ was here on earth, He could compassionately minister to the people around Him. How are we recipients of His compassion now? Read Psalms 86:15 and 145:8 and Lamentations 3:22 and 23.

9. As believers become more like Christ (Ephesians 4:13), our lives should reflect Christlike qualities. What have you learned about Christ's compassion for people that you need to apply to your own life? Do you seek to minister to hurting people, or do you more often turn away from them?

10. Discuss with the other members of your class or study group how you could reach out to a hurting segment of society and demonstrate the love and compassion of Christ. Depending on what is available in your community, here are some places to consider: a gospel mission; a soup kitchen or food distribution center; a shelter for battered wives and children; an AIDS clinic; a home for the aged.

He Sought Them Alone:
Evangelization

"For the Son of man is come to seek and to save that which was lost" (Luke 19:10).

T he Lord God of Heaven is compassionate. Not only does He have compassion for mankind, but He also has a plan for the complete redemption and restoration of people. It is important for us to listen to what God tells us about that plan.

After Adam and Eve sinned, God covered them with the skins of animals. That sacrifice covered, but did not take away, their sin.

Jesus came into the world according to God's plan to redeem sinners: "Wherefore when he cometh into the world, he saith, Sacrifice and offering thou wouldest not, but a body hast thou prepared me: . . . Then said I, Lo, I come (in the volume of the book it is written of me,) to do thy will, O God" (Hebrews 10:5, 7). The awfulness of sin required something greater than animal sacrifices to avert God's righteous anger. The Lord Jesus Christ came willingly to offer Himself: "For the Son of man is come to seek and to save that which was lost" (Luke 19:10).

Getting Started

1. a. What is the most important material thing you've ever lost?

b. What, if anything, did you do to try to find what you had lost?

c. If you were unable to find the thing you lost, how did you manage without it?

2. Read Luke 19:1–10. How far was Christ willing to go to find those who were lost?

Searching the Scriptures

3. What do Luke 4:18 and 19 reveal about how Jesus would carry out His ministry?

Jesus preached repentance, which is a change of mind, of attitude, of purpose.

4. What do the following passages teach about what is involved in true repentance?

a. 1 Thessalonians 1:9

b. Romans 6:11–13

5. a. Read Luke 18:9–14. Explain the difference in the two men.

b. Read Luke 18:18–25. Why might it be hard for a rich man to enter God's kingdom?

6. For what reason did Jesus pronounce judgment on the cities as recorded in Matthew 11:20–24?

Jesus preached, "Repent: for the kingdom of heaven is at hand" (Matthew 4:17). He thus proclaimed a negative message, repent, and a postive theme, the kingdom of heaven.

7. According to Jesus, when was the kingdom going to arrive (Matthew 4:17; Luke 4:17–21; 17:21; "within you" means "within your midst")?

Increasingly the message of Jesus was Himself. The Lord Jesus Christ is the revelation of God's grace and the One through Whom all blessings come. In a way, He alone *is* the gospel.

8. Jesus ministered to many people. Complete the chart on page 34 to better understand Jesus' ministry.

	To whom and how did Jesus minister in this passage?	How did the people respond?
Matthew 15:30, 31		
Mark 2:1–12		
Luke 7:11–16		
Luke 8:1–4		
Luke 13:10–17		

Jesus said that He had come to seek and to save the lost. He constantly showed His concern for individuals as much as for multitudes. His encounter with Zacchaeus is one example.

9. Read Luke 19:1–10. a. What kind of man was Zacchaeus?

b. What was it about Jesus that might have appealed to a man like Zacchaeus?

c. What evidence of repentance do you see in Zacchaeus?

10. Read Matthew 10:5 and 6 and 15:24. a. Why did Jesus minister primarily to Jews?

  b. While Jesus ministered primarily to Jews, He did not reject all the Gentiles who turned to Him. Why did Jesus respond to the Gentiles in these passages: Matthew 8:5–10; 15:22–28?

11. What is God's plan for reaching the world with the gospel since Christ has come? Read Matthew 28:19 and 20, Romans 10:12–17, and 1 Thessalonians 1:8.

Making It Personal

12. List a dozen people in your sphere of influence. These are people with whom you have direct contact on a regular or fairly regular basis; e.g., neighbors; attendant at the dry cleaner's; child's schoolteacher.

13. Look at your list. How many of those people need to know the Savior? Put a check mark by those names. What *specific* things can you do that might eventually lead to their salvation?

14. What is your church's involvement in world evangelization? You should recognize this involvement as an extension of yourself as you pray for and give toward these ministries. List the things your church does to take the gospel to people around the world.

He Taught Alone:
Education

"The disciple is not above his master: but every one that is perfect shall be as his master" (Luke 6:40).

The disciples had the distinct privilege of being associated with Jesus on a close, personal basis for over three years. The experience changed their lives. Jesus fully trained them, and in many ways they were like Him. The Lord Jesus Christ continues to teach us by the revelation of Himself through the Word of God and by the Holy Spirit. But just absorbing the information is not enough. We must also be like Christ and disciple others.

Getting Started

1. Think of a teacher who has influenced your life. What was it about that teacher that made an impression on you?

2. How much of a teacher's impact comes through formal teaching?

3. What other factors can cause us to become like our teachers?

Searching the Scriptures

4. Many people followed Jesus, but He chose twelve, whom we know as the disciples. For what purposes did Jesus choose those twelve men (Mark 3:13–19)?

Why did Jesus choose only twelve? That was a manageable number to which He could give concentrated effort. He wished to develop in them leadership skills and commitment that would enable them to continue His work after His departure.

5. What did Jesus do before He called these men (Luke 6:12, 13)?

6. How did the following men respond when Jesus called them?

a. Simon (Peter) and Andrew (Mark 1:16–18)

b. James and John (Mark 1:19, 20)

c. Matthew (Matthew 9:9)

d. Philip (John 1:43–46)

The disciples' *curiosity* about Christ blossomed into *conviction* concerning Him. Their conviction then led to *commitment,* or a lifestyle of becoming like Him. Jesus developed their commitment through instruction, example, and experience.

7. Luke 6:20–49 is one example of Jesus' teaching His disciples. List three themes that Jesus developed in this discourse.

8. In each of the following passages, identify the *characteristic* that Jesus modeled for His disciples.

a. Luke 13:34; 22:50, 51

b. Luke 7:11–15

c. Mark 1:35; Luke 11:1

d. Luke 9:51

9. How did Jesus provide experience for His disciples as recorded in Mark 6:7–13?

10. How did the ministry of the Twelve resemble the ministry of Christ (Mark 6:12, 13)?

Making It Personal

11. The stages in becoming a fully devoted follower of Christ are curiosity, conviction, and commitment. Which of the following statements best describes you?

___ I am *curious* about Jesus Christ and am willing to learn more.

___ I am *convinced* that Jesus is the Son of God and my Savior, but I am not wholly committed to living my life for Him.

___ I am *committed* to living for Christ and growing in likeness to Him.

If you checked curious or convinced, you may want to talk to your pastor, group leader, or other mature believer about how you can move on to the point of being a committed follower of Jesus Christ.

12. a. Your Bible study helped you discover that Jesus developed His disciples' commitment through instruction, example, and experience. Most Bible-believing churches are concerned about discipleship. How does your church provide the instruction that helps people come to know Christ and grow in Him?

b. Who are the people you look to as examples of mature Christians?

c. What experiences are provided through your church to help you mature, or grow, in Christ?

13. Write a brief paragraph that summarizes your level of commitment to Christ and the things you are doing to foster your personal growth in Christlikeness.

He Was Glorified Alone: *Transfiguration*

"While he yet spake, behold, a bright cloud over-shadowed them: and behold a voice out of the cloud, which said, This is my beloved Son, in whom I am well pleased; hear ye him" (Matthew 17:5).

Who is Jesus? The Pharisees and Sadducees had been debating that question and had asked Jesus for a sign that would identify Him (Matthew 16:1). Jesus Himself asked the disciples what people were saying about Him. To cause His disciples to personally respond to what they had been seeing and hearing, Jesus asked the important question, "But whom say ye that I am?" The transfiguration of Jesus Christ helped answer that question.

Getting Started

1. Name four people in the news today and the reason each one is receiving public recognition.

A political figure

A sports figure

An international figure

An entertainment figure

2. Which of those famous people would you want to meet and why?

Searching the Scriptures

3. a. What kind of attention did Jesus receive as His ministry became known? See Matthew 7:28, 29; 9:8, 33, 34; 12:14, 23; 13:54–57; 14:33; 15:10–12, 31.

b. What caused these differences of opinion about Him?

4. When Jesus asked the disciples, "But whom say ye that I am?" (Matthew 16:15), Peter responded, "Thou art the Christ, the Son of the living God" (v. 16). What does Peter's reply say about Jesus?

a. His mission

b. His true nature

5. Previously, when Jesus asked, "Whom do men say that I the Son of man am?" (Matthew 16:13), the disciples answered, "Some say that thou art John the Baptist: some, Elias; and others, Jeremias, or one of the prophets" (v. 14). Why did the disciples' answer differ from the people's concerning Jesus' identity?

In Matthew 16:28 and Mark 9:1 and 2 Jesus declared that some of His disciples would live to see Him in His kingdom. Six days after that promise, He selected three disciples to go with Him to a private place on Mount Hermon, where He fulfilled the promise.

6. Read Matthew 17:1–8, Mark 9:3–8, and Luke 9:29–36. Peter wrote at a later time about this experience (2 Peter 1:16–18). How did the transfiguration of Jesus Christ demonstrate each of the following?

a. His majesty

b. His honor

c. His excellent glory

7. During the Transfiguration, how did God

a. affirm Christ's righteousness?

b. confirm Jesus' dedication to doing the Father's will?

8. What did the three disciples learn about the kingdom at the Transfiguration?

9. How would seeing Jesus Christ transfigured before them have encouraged Peter, James, and John to persevere during the trials to come (Acts 12:1–4; 2 Peter 1:14; Revelation 1:9)?

10. As Jesus and the three came down off the mountain, Jesus told them not to say anything about the experience until after He had risen from the dead (Matthew 17:9; Mark 9:9). Why do you think He required their silence until then? (Keep in mind that Jesus had been telling them that He would die soon.)

Making It Personal

Peter and the other true disciples confessed their faith in Christ before they saw His glory. They did not have perfect understanding, but that did not cause them to delay or doubt.

11. What is the condition of your faith?

> a. Have you *trusted* Jesus Christ as your Savior?

> b. Do you *look to* Him as your Master?

> c. Do you *depend upon* Him as your Guide?

> d. Do you *obey* Him and reverence Him as your Lord?

12. While you have never seen Jesus in His glory, you have the Biblical record, which includes eyewitness accounts. How can you share your personal "eyewitness" account (your salvation testimony) with those around you?

13. a. One day we will see the Lord in all His glory. How should this truth affect your life right now? Read 1 John 2:28 and 3:2 and 3.

> b. How should this truth affect your thoughts and feelings about death? Read 2 Corinthians 5:1–8, 2 Timothy 4:6–8, and 1 Thessalonians 4:14–18.

He Was Rejected Alone:
Opposition

"Yea, and all that will live godly in Christ Jesus shall suffer persecution. But evil men and seducers shall wax worse and worse, deceiving, and being deceived. But continue thou in the things which thou hast learned and hast been assured of, knowing of whom thou hast learned them" (2 Timothy 3:12–14).

We have seen Jesus' compassion as He went about doing good. We've also read His gracious words and have learned from both His words and His example. We have also read about the glory of Jesus Christ as witnessed by Peter, James, and John. And we have seen how people marveled and gave God the glory for the things they saw and heard in Christ's ministry. But in this lesson we will discover the opposition Jesus faced.

Getting Started

1. a. Name some well-known opponents or rivals (e.g., in sports, in politics).

b. What causes and builds rivalries such as the ones you named?

c. Why are some rivalries merely good-natured competition, while others are hostile or even violent?

2. a. Have you ever pursued a right course of action or taken a stand for what is right only to face opposition? If so, describe the situation.

b. How did you feel as the object of opposition or criticism?

Searching the Scriptures

3. Jesus faced opposition in everything He sought to do. The person ultimately behind that opposition was Satan. His long-standing opposition to God and His plan began before the Garden in Eden. In each passage, identify how Satan opposed God.

a. Isaiah 14:12–14

b. Genesis 3:1–7

c. Matthew 2:1–18 (Herod as Satan's agent)

Following Jesus' baptism, Satan intensified his warfare against Jesus. However, Jesus showed no hesitation in facing this opponent.

4. Satan tried to attack Jesus, but he went away defeated. In fact, Jesus told him, "Get thee hence" (Matthew 4:10).

a. Why did Satan tempt Jesus (Matthew 4:1–10)?

b. Why did Satan back off (v. 10)?

c. What does Luke 4:13 reveal about Satan's attitude toward Christ?

5. Identify Jesus' attack on Satan's power and influence in the following passages. Explain how each attack or confrontation broke Satan's hold on people.

a. Matthew 8:16

b. Matthew 9:2–6

c. Matthew 10:1

d. Matthew 7:15; 16:6; Luke 12:1

6. Why did Jesus' works cause some people to glorify God but others to be critical and resentful? See Mark 2:5–12. Compare Luke 4:16–22 with verses 23–29. Also see Matthew 12:22–24 as an example of conflicting responses to Jesus' ministry.

7. In the following passages, identify the person or people who opposed Jesus and explain why they may have felt threatened by Jesus' words or deeds.

a. Mark 3:1–6

b. Mark 5:1–17

c. Luke 13:10–16

8. How do the following messianic psalms (psalms that foretell things about Jesus Christ) indicate Jesus' feelings about the opposition to Him and His ministry?

a. Psalm 22:9–21

b. Psalm 35:19–22

c. Psalm 69:7–9

9. According to 1 Peter 2:21–24, why did Christ endure all that opposition?

Making It Personal

10. Jesus countered Satan's power and influence in people's lives with His divine power. According to Acts 1:8 and Romans 1:16, what power is available to believers as we seek to help people who are in Satan's grip?

11. The Pharisees were religious men, but they opposed the Lord. Think of "religious" people and groups in our world today who oppose the things of Christ. How do these people or groups show their opposition to Biblical Christianity?

12. Read 1 Peter 2:21 and 23 again. If we follow the example of Christ, what should be our response when we meet with unfair criticism or even hostility?

Lesson 8

He Offered Alone:
Presentation

"And Jesus entered into Jerusalem, and into the temple: and when he had looked round about upon all things, and now the eventide was come, he went out unto Bethany with the twelve" (Mark 11:11).

I t's great to be a winner! Fans want to see a team win, and the crowds increase when the team has a winning streak. When they get close to winning the pennant—and perhaps later, the World Series—baseball lovers fill the stands; not one empty seat can be found. People today are no different from those who lived two thousand years ago. As Jesus' reputation spread, people wanted to see Him, to be where the action was. Multitudes accompanied him into Jerusalem, shouting, "Hosanna; Blessed is he that cometh in the name of the Lord" (Mark 11:9). But soon everything went back to normal. Jesus returned to His ministry, and the Pharisees, to their criticism of Him.

Getting Started

1. What are some commonly recognized warning signals, and what do they mean?

a. in your neighborhood (e.g., a garbage truck backing up may send a warning beep)

b. in your home (e.g., the microwave beeps to let you know the cooking cycle has finished)

c. in your body (e.g., shivering warns you that your body needs heat)

2. a. What warnings guard and guide believers spiritually?

b. Why do we need such warnings?

As the opposition to Christ's ministry increased, so did His warnings to His disciples.

Searching the Scriptures

3. Once the disciples recognized Jesus' deity, He began teaching them that He would suffer rejection by the Jewish leaders (Mark 8:27–31). Why did He wait until that time to warn the disciples?

4. Read Matthew 17:1–9; then answer the following questions.

   a. Why might the Transfiguration have led the disciples to believe that Jesus was about to reveal His glory to the world and establish His earthly kingdom?

   b. What did Jesus say to Peter, James, and John to help them understand that something else had to take place first?

5. Mark 9:31 and 32 say, "For he taught his disciples, and said unto them, The Son of man is delivered into the hands of men, and they shall kill him; and after that he is killed, he shall rise the third day. But they understood not that saying, and were afraid to ask him." Why wouldn't the disciples have understood Jesus' clear teaching here? See Isaiah 6:9 and 10.

6. Read Matthew 10:34, Mark 10:32–38, and Luke 9:22–24. a. What in these verses reveals that Jesus would be mistreated, not glorified, as King?

b. What in these verses indicates that the disciples didn't get Jesus' point?

The disciples clung to the hope common among the people that Jesus, as the Messiah, would destroy His enemies during His earthly ministry; they did not receive this idea from Jesus. In spite of His frequent explanations that He must die, the disciples had their thoughts fixed on the kingdom and what it would mean to them.

7. Jesus told a parable to clear up the misconception that the kingdom would appear immediately. Read Luke 19:11–27, and explain how the parable relates to Jesus in the following points.

a. Timing of the kingdom

b. Duty of servants

c. Servants' accountability

d. Setup of kingdom

Both Jesus and John the Baptist preached, "The kingdom of heaven is at hand" (Matthew 3:2; 4:17). It is legitimate to ask, If the kingdom was at hand, what happened to postpone it until after Christ's return?

8. Another parable helps answer that question. Read Luke 20:9–19. a. In the parable the nobleman represents God the Father. Who or what is represented by these other aspects of the parable?

Vineyard

Husbandmen/stewards

Far country

Servants

Heir

b. Why was the kingdom postponed?

When the Pharisees decided that Jesus was a threat to their plans and began plotting His murder, they were plainly rejecting the terms of God's kingdom (Luke 20:9–19). From that point Jesus ceased proclaiming the kingdom and began teaching of His approaching death.

9. a. How does Luke 20:19 relate to the parable in verses 9–16?

b. According to verse 14, what was the motive in disposing of the rightful heir?

The offer of the kingdom was contingent on reception of the King. He was "in the midst" of them, but the Jews did not recognize or receive Him, so the offer was postponed.

10. What does Acts 1:6 reveal about the disciples' attitude toward the kingdom?

11. Read Matthew 21:1–6. a. How do the events of verses 4 and 5 fulfill the prophecies of Isaiah 62:11 and Zechariah 9:9?

b. According to Matthew 21:15 and 16 and Luke 19:39, not everyone who saw the entrance of Jesus was pleased with the scene. What was the objection?

Making It Personal

12. What the people—and the disciples—expected of Jesus was not the correct expectation. What are some incorrect expectations people may have today about Biblical truths? One example would be that when a person becomes a Christian, his or her life will be free of difficulties.

13. Use a Bible concordance (or your memory) to locate Scripture passages that correct the wrong expectations you noted above. Jot a reference or two by each of your entries. For example, John 16:33 is a verse that indicates believers will have tribulation in this world.

14. The most incorrect expectation of all is to think that good works are the basis of salvation. If you have been trusting in your good works, now is the time to bring your expectation in line with the Word of God. Read these verses: John 3:16; Acts 4:12; 16:31; Romans 10:9; Ephesians 2:8, 9; Titus 3:5. Trust in Christ alone for your salvation. Talk to your pastor, group leader, or a Christian friend about your decision.

He Prayed Alone:
Intercession

"Then said I, Lo, I come (in the volume of the book it is written of me,) to do thy will, O God" **(Hebrews 10:7).**

An Internet search on the word "prayer" reveals the universality of prayer. You could find a prayer of the Iroquois culture, a Tibetan mantra on a digital prayer wheel, or a site run by Irish Jesuits. You could find a page on how to combine herbology with prayer. You could learn about centering, or contemplative prayer, which "is the opening of mind and heart—our whole being—to God, the Ultimate Mystery, beyond thoughts, words and emotions, whom we know by faith is within us, closer than breathing, thinking, feeling and choosing; even closer than consciousness itself." Or you could join the Presidential Prayer Team. You could find a prayer site for couples with infertility problems. Or you could study prayers in a collection of "the great prayer classics from spiritual traditions around the world." And the list goes on and on and on. . . .

The point is that people today are praying. You'll probably hear your neighbors mention praying for this or that. You'll certainly hear about prayer in church and on Christian radio and TV programs. You'll even hear American news anchors and political leaders say, "Our prayers are with _____." But does the fact that many are praying mean that their prayers are getting anywhere? that the prayers please God?

that they correspond to His will? that He is answering them?

In this lesson we will study the prayers of Jesus Christ, the God-Man, and what we can learn about prayer from His teaching and His example.

Getting Started

1. How do people learn to pray?

2. How have the following factors influenced your own knowledge of prayer?

   a. Trial and error

   b. Examples of prayer in the Bible

   c. Books or studies on prayer

   d. Listening to others pray

3. What area of your prayer life do you need to develop?

Search the Scriptures

4. The disciples asked Jesus to teach them to pray. What seems to have motivated the disciples' request (Luke 11:1)?

5. Read the model prayer that Jesus gave the disciples (Luke 11:2–4; Matthew 6:9–13).

a. What do you learn about God from this prayer?

b. What do you learn about sin?

c. What do you learn about human relationships?

d. How much of this prayer deals with a person's material needs? What does that tell you?

e. What does the close of this prayer indicate to you?

f. What does this prayer indicate to you about what a praying
person's priorities should be?

6. Read Matthew 6:5–8. a. Jesus warned against "vain [empty] rep-
etitions" (v. 7). How does this warning relate to Christians' quoting of
the prayer in Matthew 6:9–13 or Luke 11:2–4?

b. In light of verses 5–8, what might be some problems in depending on other people for our understanding of prayer and
how to pray?

7. What do you conclude about prayer from Jesus' example in Matthew 14:23, Mark 1:35 and 14:32–35, and Luke 6:12 and 13 and from
His teaching in Matthew 6:5–8?

Jesus told two parables about prayer and used characters who are the opposite of God.

8. a. Read Luke 11:5–13. How does God the Father differ from the reluctant friend?

b. Read Luke 18:1–8. How does God the Father differ from the unjust judge?

9. Read Luke 18:9–14. What do you learn from this parable and the ones in 11:5–13 and 18:1–8 about the following areas?

a. The praying person's attitude

b. Delays

c. God's attitude toward the praying person

10. Read each of the following passages and identify the insight about prayer that Jesus' example provides.

    a. Matthew 9:38; 10:1

    b. Matthew 19:13, 14

    c. Luke 6:12, 13

    d. Luke 22:46

    e. Luke 23:34

A great example of Jesus' prayer life is His prayer in Gethsemane before His death.

11. Read Matthew 26:36–44, Mark 14:32–41, and Luke 22:39–46.

    a. What emotions are expressed in these accounts?

    b. What desire(s) did Christ express in His prayer?

c. What commitment did He express?

Making It Personal

12. In all areas of our lives—prayer included—the Lord Jesus is our supreme example. Look at your answers to the items in question 10. How does your prayer life measure up to the example of Christ? Complete the following statement, basing your answer on the truths in question 10. I want my prayer life to be more like Christ's; therefore I will _____

_____

_____ .

13. a. Think of Jesus' prayer in the Garden of Gethsemane. What is the difference between *resignation* to God's will and *submission* to His will?

b. How can we submit ourselves to God in prayer?

14. What is one change you will make in your prayer life in the week ahead?

He Stood Alone:
Accusation

"He was oppressed, and he was afflicted, yet he opened not his mouth: he is brought as a lamb to the slaughter, and as a sheep before her shearers is dumb, so he openeth not his mouth. He was taken from prison and from judgment: and who shall declare his generation? for he was cut off out of the land of the living: for the transgression of my people was he stricken" (Isaiah 53:7, 8).

The most strange, cruel, and illegal trial in history was the trial of Jesus Christ. He was charged with six different "crimes," two under Jewish law (which were inadmissible to a Roman court) and four under Roman law. His accusers presented no evidence—only allegations. As strange as it may seem, He was acquitted four times yet was eventually condemned and crucified. So much for justice at the hands of mankind! That trial was part of God's plan, and Jesus Christ, the Son of God, stood accused *alone.*

Getting Started

1. List three famous courtroom dramas in our society (real or fictional).

71

2. What influence have these real or fictional dramas had on our society's view of law and justice?

Searching the Scriptures

3. After reading Luke 6:11, 11:53 and 54, 13:31, and 19:47, trace the course of antagonism toward Jesus.

4. a. What people felt this hostility toward Christ?

    b. Why do you suppose they plotted against Jesus? (See Matthew 9:3.)

5. How did the events of Jesus' arrest reflect His steadfastness toward His mission (Matthew 26:47–56)?

6. What common element of an arrest was missing from Jesus' arrest?

The soldiers took Jesus to Annas (John 18:13), who had been the high priest and was the father-in-law of Caiaphas, the current high priest. Annas couldn't get anything out of Jesus, so he sent Jesus to Caiaphas (v. 24).

7. Read the accounts of Jesus' appearance before Caiaphas and the Sanhedrin (Jewish religious leaders): Matthew 26:57—27:1; Mark 14:53—15:1; Luke 22:54–71. a. What did Jesus say throughout these ordeals?

   b. What is the significance of His almost complete silence? Read
   Isaiah 53:7.

Nothing about these procedures was just: the council met at a prohibited hour; the witnesses against Jesus were found to be false but went unpunished; Jesus confessed willingly, which meant His confession was inadmissible, but the rulers used it against Him to find Him guilty of blasphemy and, therefore, worthy of death; they never considered He could be telling the truth; according to Jewish law, if a capital charge was made, the death sentence couldn't be carried out until twenty-four hours had passed, but the rulers ignored procedure; no defense was presented; no one spoke up against the injustice.

8. What was the rulers' purpose in holding these trials?

The council later took the next step: turning Jesus over to the Roman governor, Pilate.

9. The Jewish officials knew that Pilate wouldn't care whether or not Jesus had blasphemed the Jewish religion. Read Matthew 27:2 and 11–14, Mark 15:1–5, and Luke 23:1–5.

    a. How did the Jewish officials evade telling Pilate why they really wanted to crucify Jesus?

    b. How did these charges differ from the one they came up with in their religious court?

    c. Pilate announced, "I find in him no fault at all" (Luke 23:4), so why didn't he release Jesus (Mark 15:15)?

Since Jesus was from Galilee, Pilate quickly arranged for Jesus to be sent to the palace where Herod stayed when in Jerusalem.

10. a. According to Luke 23:8 and 9, what was Herod's chief interest in Jesus?

    b. Why did Herod do nothing about the civil charge against Jesus but merely return Him to Pilate (vv. 10–12)?

11. Who stood with Jesus Christ during those hours of lies and abuse (Matthew 26:31, 56)?

Making It Personal

12. Have you ever been falsely accused of something? How did you feel? Did anyone stick up for you? How was the situation resolved?

Whatever personal experiences we may have had, none of them compare to what the Lord Jesus endured for us.

13. You have probably heard or read accounts of people who have been martyred for their faith in Christ. At what times would their experiences have been similar to those Jesus endured?

14. You will probably not die as a martyr. But as a follower of Jesus Christ, you are commanded to stand for Him. (See, for instance, 1 Corinthians 16:13 and Ephesians 6:11 and 13.) a. What does it mean to stand for Christ?

b. What are some situations in which you need to stand for Christ?

c. What have you learned from the example of Christ that will help you be bold to stand for Him?

He Died Alone:
Crucifixion

"He was wounded for our transgressions, he was bruised for our iniquities: the chastisement of our peace was upon him; and with his stripes we are healed" (Isaiah 53:5).

The cross is a common symbol in churches and on cars, clothes, jewelry—even graffiti! In a general sense it suggests martyrdom, selflessness, or religion. But comparatively few people realize that the empty cross depicts the single most important event in history.

Getting Started

1. Have you ever started to do something voluntarily when someone turned around and ordered you to do the very thing you were going to do anyway? How did that make you feel?

2. Have you ever done anything self-sacrificially and received no commendation or thanks for what you did? How did that make you feel?

Jesus Christ voluntarily gave His life for mankind. Sometimes we lose sight of that fact: He laid down His life; no one took it from Him. Nevertheless, plenty of people abused Him and were responsible for His crucifixion. Then, too, all of us sent Him to the cross, because He went there to die for *our* sins. The question is, What are we doing in response to His sacrifice?

Searching the Scriptures

3. Jesus' abuse did not end with the mockery of His trials and His treatment by Herod's soldiers. Read Matthew 27:27–31 and 37, Mark 15:26, and Luke 23:38.

    a. What accusation did Pilate's soldiers pick up from the trial?

    b. How did they mock Jesus?

4. a. Read Luke 23:27–32. What was the focus of Jesus' concern?

    b. Who probably heard what He said?

    c. What effect should His statement have had on those who heard?

5. At the execution site Jesus was offered wine mixed with gall, apparently designed to dull the pain. How did Jesus respond (Matthew 27:34)?

6. What was ironic about Jesus' "crime," which was written above the cross: "THIS IS THE KING OF THE JEWS" (Luke 23:38; cf. Matthew 2:1, 2)?

7. Jesus made seven statements from the cross. Write each statement and the subject of each one.

   a. Luke 23:34

   b. Luke 23:43

   c. John 19:26, 27

   d. Matthew 27:46

   e. John 19:28

   f. John 19:30

g. Luke 23:46

8. According to Matthew 27:46, Galatians 3:13, and Hebrews 2:9, what did Jesus Christ suffer when He died?

9. a. Matthew records three extraordinary events that occurred when Jesus Christ gave up His spirit (27:50–52). What were they?

b. What impression did these events make on a Roman centurion (v. 54)?

10. a. Read Mark 10:45. How had Christ defined His ministry?

b. What was Christ able to do that all the sacrifices of all human history could not do? Read Hebrews 9:26 and 10:4–12.

Making It Personal

11. One's devotional life can often be enriched by keeping a hymn-book near one's Bible. If you have a hymnbook, take time to carefully and prayerfully read the words that others have written to try to capture the meaning of the death of Christ. Here are some hymns to get you started: "Saved by the Blood"; "Nothing But the Blood"; "There Is a Fountain"; "Alas! and Did My Savior Bleed?"; "O Sacred Head, Now Wounded"; "He Was Wounded for Our Transgressions"; "When I Survey the Wondrous Cross."

12. The cross was important to the apostle Paul. Choose one of these verses from Paul's epistles to memorize: 1 Corinthians 1:18; Galatians 2:20; or Galatians 6:14. Quote the verse of your choice often as a reminder of what the cross means to you.

13. The next time your church observes the Lord's Supper, ask God to remind you of the Scriptures you have studied in this lesson and to make the suffering of the cross meaningful to you in a new way.

14. It is possible to have come this far in a study of the life of Christ and still not have received Jesus Christ as your Savior. He died for *you,* and He longs for *you* to receive the gift of eternal salvation (Romans 6:23; John 1:12). You can do that today. "For whosoever shall call upon the name of the Lord shall be saved" (Romans 10:13).

Lesson 12

He Arose Alone:
Resurrection

"Now is Christ risen from the dead, and become the firstfruits of them that slept. For since by man came death, by man came also the resurrection of the dead. For as in Adam all die, even so in Christ shall all be made alive" (1 Corinthians 15:20–22).

Have you ever wondered where you'd be if Jesus hadn't died on the cross? How about if He hadn't risen from the grave? In 1 Corinthians 15:14 and 17 Paul pointed out how much trouble believers would be in if Jesus hadn't risen from the dead: "If Christ be not risen, then is our preaching vain, and your faith is also vain. . . . Ye are yet in your sins." It really boils down to this: every believer's standing with God depends on whether God accepted Jesus' sacrifice on the cross. The resurrection proves that God the Father did accept the sacrifice of God the Son. Without it, believers have nothing to believe in—we're still dead in our sins.

Getting Started

1. How does a nation deal with the unexpected death of one of its leaders, heroes, or superstars?

2. Do you remember how you felt during the first few hours and days after a loved one passed away? What memories stand out to you about that time?

3. What do "B.C." and "A.D." stand for?

Searching the Scriptures

4. Matthew 2:1–10 tells us that a star marked Jesus' birth. What things marked His death? Review Matthew 27:45 and 50–53.

5. What do Galatians 1:4 and 2:20, Ephesians 5:25, 1 Timothy 2:6, and Titus 2:14 reveal about Jesus' death?

6. Joseph of Arimathea asked Pilate for Jesus' body. What does the Bible tell us about this man? Read Matthew 27:57–60; Mark 15:42–46; John 19:38–42?

7. What precautions did Pilate and the Jewish rulers take to ensure the integrity of the tomb? Why did they do this? See Matthew 27:62–66.

8. a. Why did Mary and the other women go to Jesus' tomb early Sunday morning (Matthew 28:1; Mark 15:47—16:2; Luke 23:55—24:1)?

b. What concern did they have about what would happen at the tomb (Mark 16:3)?

9. How do Joseph of Arimathea's actions, the women's actions, and the resurrection-morning events preclude the following possibilities?

a. The Roman soldiers fell asleep, and Jesus' disciples took His body (Matthew 28:11–15).

b. Jesus wasn't really dead; He swooned and then revived (Mark 15:42–45).

c. The women and the disciples went to the wrong tomb, found it empty, and told the story that Jesus had risen from the dead (Luke 24:1–12).

10. How did the disciples first respond to the empty tomb (Matthew 28:17; Mark 16:14; Luke 24:12)?

11. Why might Jesus have shown Himself to the following people after His resurrection?

a. Mary Magdalene (Mark 16:9–11)

b. The other women (Matthew 28:1, 8–10)

c. Two followers on the Emmaus road (Luke 24:13–32)

d. The eleven disciples (Luke 24:36–48; John 20:19–29)

e. Five hundred believers at one time (1 Corinthians 15:6)

12. What difference did Jesus' resurrection make

a. to the disciples (Acts 2:22–24, 32)?

b. to prophecy (Acts 2:25–31)?

Making It Personal

13. The resurrection is more than a doctrine to believe; it is a motivation for living. a. What does it mean to live for Him Who died for us and rose again (2 Corinthians 5:14, 15)?

   b. Read 1 Corinthians 15:51–58. Because Christ has had victory over the grave, what are we to do?

14. Jesus said, "Because I live, ye shall live also" (John 14:19). How does the resurrection of Christ bring us comfort when a Christian dies?

15. How does Jesus' resurrection assure your own resurrection? Read 1 Corinthians 15:20–23.

Lesson 13

One Solitary Life:
A Review

"Jesus Christ of Nazareth, whom ye crucified, whom God raised from the dead, . . . Neither is there salvation in any other: for there is none other name under heaven given among men, whereby we must be saved" (Acts 4:10, 12).

Our study has shown how the Lord Jesus Christ was truly, fully man yet was set apart, solitary, unique in His life and work. Never has there been another man like Jesus, and there never will be. He did what no one else could do: provide deliverance from sin. Jesus was unique because He was both God and man. In this lesson we will review specific aspects of the life of Jesus Christ that make His life *One Solitary Life.*

Getting Started

1. Read the familiar essay "One Solitary Life"; then respond to the questions that follow it.

"He was born in an obscure village, the child of a simple peasant woman. He grew up in another obscure village, where He worked in a carpenter shop until He was thirty. Then for three years He was an itinerant preacher.

"He never had a family. He never owned a home. He never set

foot inside a big city. He never traveled [more than] two hundred miles from the place He was born, and where He did go, He usually walked. He never wrote a book. He never held political office. He did none of the things we usually associate with greatness.

"While He was still a young man, the tide of popular opinion turned against Him. His friends deserted Him. He was turned over to His enemies and went through the mockery of a trial. He was nailed to a cross between two thieves. While He was dying, His executioners gambled for the only piece of property He had in this world—and that was His robe.

"When He was dead, He was taken down and laid in a borrowed grave provided by compassionate friends.

"Nineteen wide centuries have come and gone, and today He is the central figure for much of the human race, the leader in the column of human progress. All the armies that ever marched, and all the navies that ever sailed, and all the parliaments that ever sat, and all the kings that ever reigned, put together, have not affected the life of man upon this earth so powerfully as this one solitary life" (James Allen Francis; 1926).

2. What point was the author trying to emphasize about the life of Christ?

3. If you were going to summarize the solitary life of Christ, what additional information would you include?

Searching the Scriptures

4. Why is the Virgin Birth important to our salvation?

5. How does the response to Jesus' birth by the following people correspond with the response of people today?

a. Mary, Joseph, Elisabeth, Simeon, Anna (Matthew 1:18–25; Luke 1:26–56; 2:21–34; 36–38)

b. Shepherds and wise men (Luke 2:8–18; Matthew 2:1–12)

c. Herod (Matthew 2:1–16)

d. Chief priests and scribes (Matthew 2:4–6)

6. Read Luke 4:1–13. a. Why might Satan have thought Jesus would yield to one of his temptations?

b. Jesus is God; the Spirit had led Him into the wilderness to be
tempted by Satan. How did Jesus use the Word of God to
battle Satan?

7. a. Why do the kinds of temptations that Satan used (the provi-
sion of bread, popularity with the world, and power over kingdoms)
work so well with people today (1 John 2:16)?

b. Why can using God's Word to defeat temptation work as well
for us as it did for Jesus (Hebrews 4:12; Psalm 119:9–11)?

8. What did Jesus want people to do after He preached to them,
taught them, or healed them (Matthew 4:17; Mark 1:14, 15; Luke 13:5)?

9. Who did Jesus come to seek and to save (John 1:29; 3:16, 17;
8:12; Romans 5:12–19)?

10. Jesus was transfigured, or changed, to reveal His glory.

a. What did the men see that revealed Jesus' glory?

　　b. What did they hear?

11. Review Lesson 7. Name some people who opposed Jesus and how Jesus responded to them.

People Opposed to Jesus	Jesus' Response to the Opposition

12. The disciples expected a victorious Messiah Who would defeat the Romans and set up an earthly Jewish kingdom. Instead, what kind of Messiah was Jesus (Matthew 16:21; 17:9, 22, 23)?

13. Before His death, Jesus prayed alone in Gethsemane (Matthew 26:36–46; Mark 14:32–42; Luke 22:39–46).

　　a. What emotions does His prayer reveal?

b. What desire(s) did Jesus express in His prayer?

c. What commitment did He express?

14. In what ways did Jesus go through His substitutionary death for us alone (Matthew 27:46, 55, 56; Mark 14:50; 15:34)?

15. In the previous lesson we learned that the resurrection is more than a doctrine to believe; it is a motivation for living. Based on 2 Corinthians 5:14 and 15 and 1 Corinthians 15:58, how should the resurrection of Christ impact your life?

Making It Personal

Jesus Christ wasn't just an effective teacher whose dogma has survived through centuries or a man whose martyrdom has been universally influential. Many people have had centuries-long, universal influence; some have been martyred. But Jesus lived a solitary life because He alone is the God-Man; He alone was fathered by God through a virgin; He alone was sinless, unable to sin; He alone made the perfect sacrifice for our sins; He alone will reign supreme in His kingdom.

16. a. Where is Jesus now (Hebrews 10:12)?

    b. What is Jesus Christ doing now? Read Hebrews 7:25 and 1 John 2:1.

    c. Why do we need this kind of ministry? See 1 John 1:7–10.

17. How has this study increased your knowledge of and love for our Savior, Jesus Christ?